Canada Aviation Museum

The Fantastic Flight of the Silver Dart

Written by Linda Brand

Illustrated by François Gauvreau

Produced by the Canada Aviation Museum
11 Aviation Parkway, P.O. Box 9724, Station T, Ottawa, Ontario K1G 5A3
1-800-463-2038   www.aviation.technomuses.ca

Library and Archives Canada Cataloguing in Publication
Brand, Linda
The Fantastic Flight of the **Silver Dart** / written by Linda Brand; illustrated by François Gauvreau.

ISBN 978-0-9811193-0-4

1. Silver Dart (Airplane)--Juvenile literature.   2. Airplanes--Canada--History--Juvenile literature.   3. Aeronautics--Canada
--History--Juvenile literature.   I. Gauvreau, François, 1961-   II. Canada Aviation Museum   III. Title.

TL523 B73 2009   j629.130971   C2009-980004-7

Designer: Mike Teixeira   Printer: Friesens, Altona, Manitoba

Cet ouvrage a été publié simultanément en français sous le titre : Le glorieux envol du **Silver Dart**

This edition of the Fantastic Flight of the **Silver Dart** book was made possible through the kind support
of Curtiss-Wright on the occasion of the centennial celebration of powered flight in Canada.

Printed in Canada

Dedicated to the memory of the members
of the **Aerial Experiment Association:**
J.A.D. McCurdy, Casey Baldwin, Thomas Selfridge,
Glenn Curtiss, Alexander Graham Bell,
and Mabel Hubbard Bell.

There once was a man called Alexander Graham Bell,
he was clever and grew a long beard — can you tell?

He kept himself busy inventing new things,
and, of course, he is famous for something that rings!

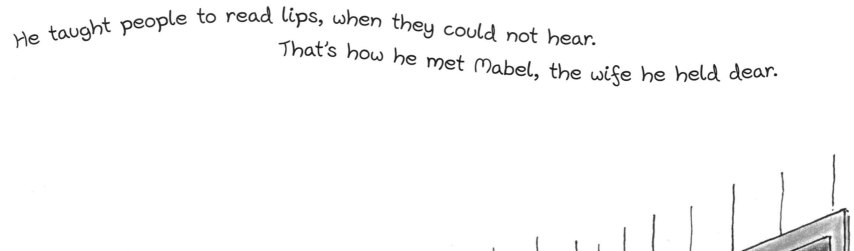

He taught people to read lips, when they could not hear.
That's how he met Mabel, the wife he held dear.

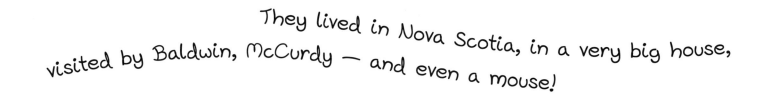

They lived in Nova Scotia, in a very big house,
visited by Baldwin, McCurdy — and even a mouse!

Beinn Bhreagh
**Baddeck
Nova Scotia**

Together they built many strange-looking kites,
which they flew in the sky at many different heights.

Some were small; others big — some could even carry a man.
Mrs. Bell always watched — she was their biggest fan!

They dreamed of machines which would fly where they wanted.
Mrs. Bell gave them money, so their wish would be granted.

They met Selfridge — and Curtiss, who made motorcycle engines, and together they formed the **Aerial Experiment Association.**

Each man built an airplane in Curtiss' shed.
First came the **Red Wing** which soon flew overhead.

Next came the **White Wing**, then the **June Bug**, too.
The men learned from each other, and knew what to do.

McCurdy next finished his big **Silver Dart.**
The Canadian was ready and eager to start.

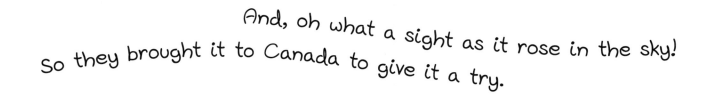

And, oh what a sight as it rose in the sky!
So they brought it to Canada to give it a try.

"Let's go to Baddeck," said Bell. "We'll make history.
It'll be the first plane to fly in our great country."

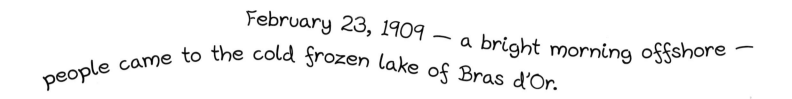

February 23, 1909 — a bright morning offshore —
people came to the cold frozen lake of Bras d'Or.

Mrs. Bell made a batch of her raspberry vinegar tea;
it helped warm the onlookers, who sipped it with glee.

People wore mufflers, thick coats, even skates,
while the Bells sat nearby in their lovely red sleigh.

The **Silver Dart** was pulled out onto the lake,
handled with care so that it would not break.

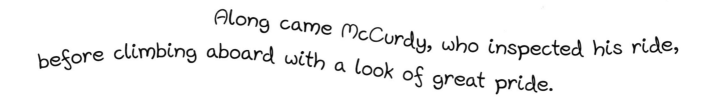

Along came McCurdy, who inspected his ride,
before climbing aboard with a look of great pride.

McCurdy held the controls good and tight.
The engine made a big bang, giving all quite a fright.

Vroom-vroom 'cross the ice the **Silver Dart** skimmed,
some skaters tried to chase it, but just couldn't win.

Up, up and away the **Silver Dart** flew,
and everyone cheered till their noses turned blue.

Mr. Bell stood up in his red sleigh and waved,
to pilot McCurdy, who felt happy and brave.

One hundred years back, our first powered aircraft took flight,

starting an aviation history that is still strong and bright.

Avro CF-105 Arrow

Bombardier Challenger 604

de Havilland Canada DHC-6 Twin Otter

So whenever you see airplanes high in the sky,
you will now know who proved that Canadians could fly!

Canadair CT-114 Tutor